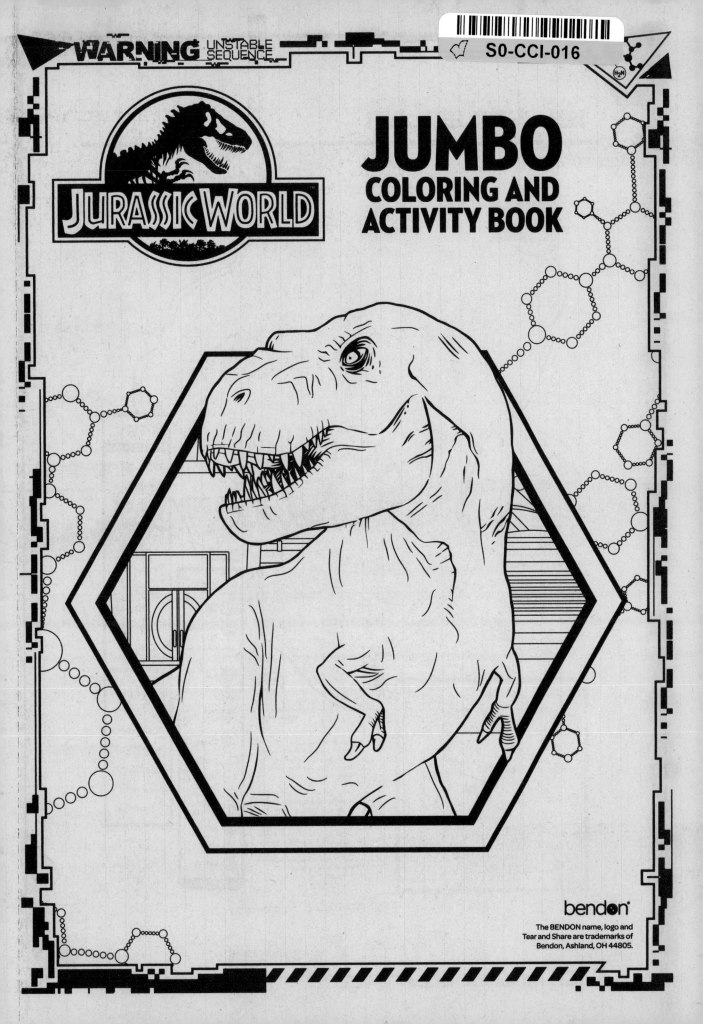

WARNING UNSTABLE SEQUENCE

JURASSIC WORLD

JUMBO
COLORING AND
ACTIVITY BOOK

bendon®

The BENDON name, logo and
Tear and Share are trademarks of
Bendon, Ashland, OH 44805.

ISLA NUBLAR

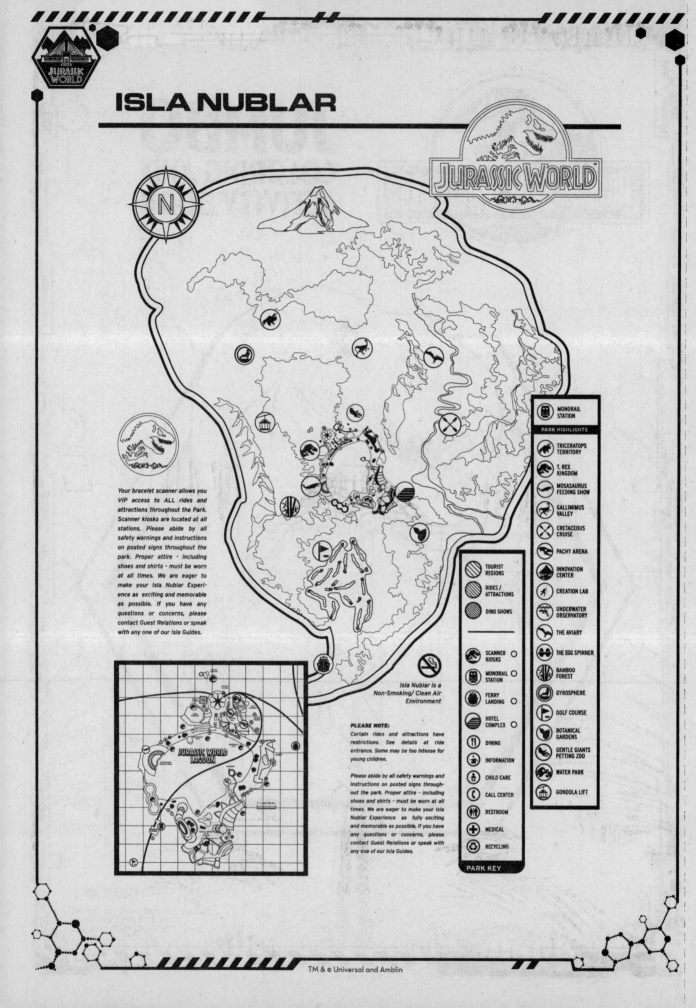

JURASSIC WORLD

Your bracelet scanner allows you VIP access to ALL rides and attractions throughout the Park. Scanner kiosks are located at all stations. Please abide by all safety warnings and instructions on posted signs throughout the park. Proper attire - including shoes and shirts - must be worn at all times. We are eager to make your Isla Nublar Experience as exciting and memorable as possible. If you have any questions or concerns, please contact Guest Relations or speak with any one of our Isla Guides.

Isla Nublar is a Non-Smoking/ Clean Air Environment

PLEASE NOTE:
Certain rides and attractions have restrictions. See details at ride entrance. Some may be too intense for young children.

Please abide by all safety warnings and instructions on posted signs throughout the park. Proper attire - including shoes and shirts - must be worn at all times. We are eager to make your Isla Nublar Experience as fully exciting and memorable as possible. If you have any questions or concerns, please contact Guest Relations or speak with any one of our Isla Guides.

JURASSIC WORLD LAGOON

PARK KEY

- TOURIST REGIONS
- RIDES / ATTRACTIONS
- DINO SHOWS
- SCANNER KIOSKS
- MONORAIL STATION
- FERRY LANDING
- HOTEL COMPLEX
- DINING
- INFORMATION
- CHILD CARE
- CALL CENTER
- RESTROOM
- MEDICAL
- RECYCLING

MONORAIL STATION

PARK HIGHLIGHTS

- TRICERATOPS TERRITORY
- T. REX KINGDOM
- MOSASAURUS FEEDING SHOW
- GALLIMIMUS VALLEY
- CRETACEOUS CRUISE
- PACHY ARENA
- INNOVATION CENTER
- CREATION LAB
- UNDERWATER OBSERVATORY
- THE AVIARY
- THE EGG SPINNER
- BAMBOO FOREST
- GYROSPHERE
- GOLF COURSE
- BOTANICAL GARDENS
- GENTLE GIANTS PETTING ZOO
- WATER PARK
- GONDOLA LIFT

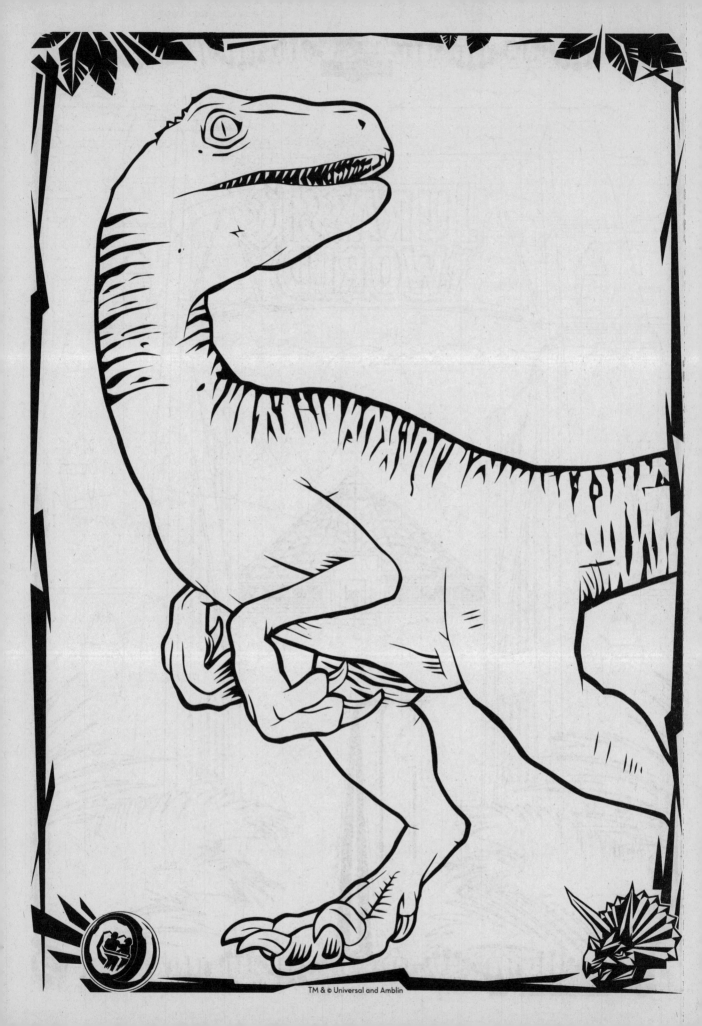

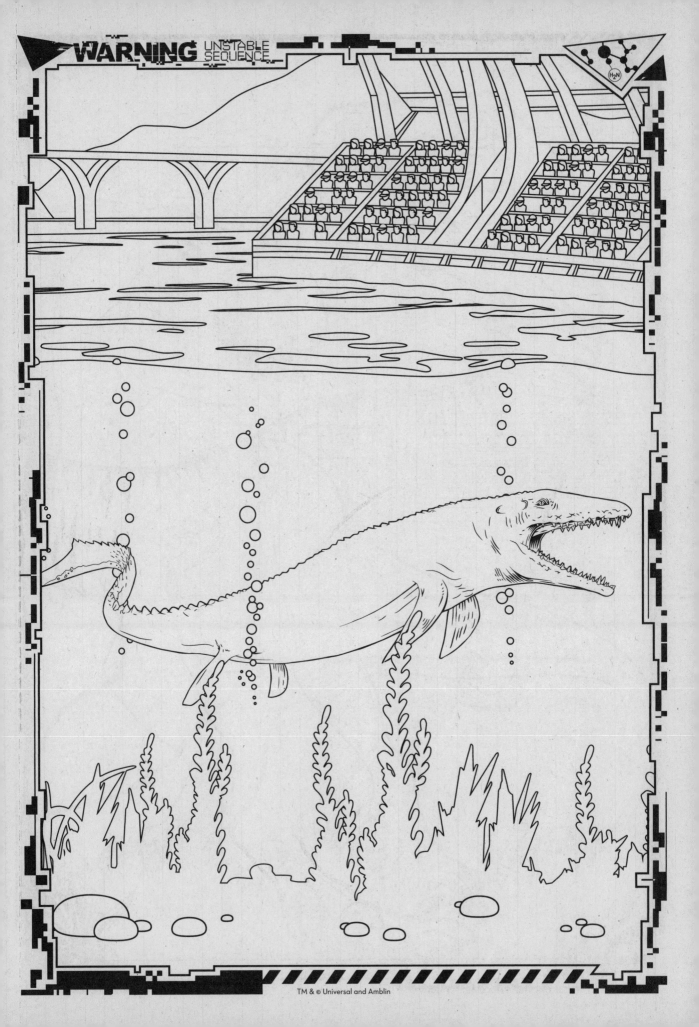

CREATION LAB

Draw a new dinosaur by splicing these two dinos together. Will yours have more armor, more teeth, or a longer tail? You decide!

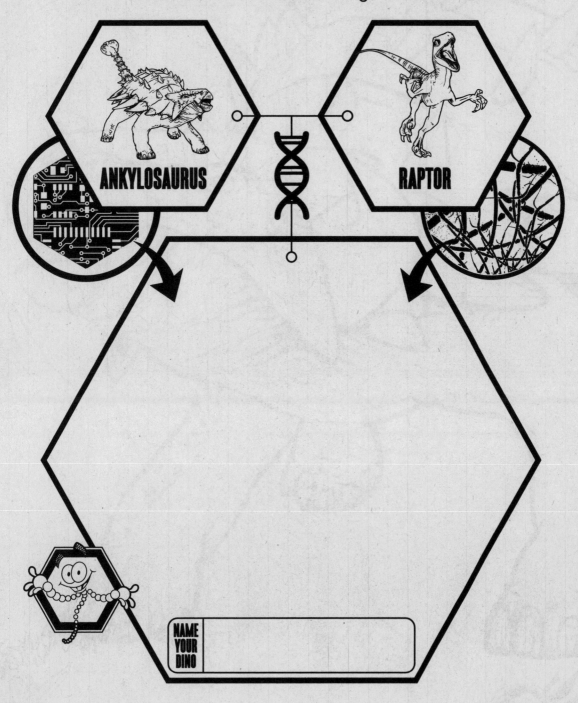

ANKYLOSAURUS

RAPTOR

NAME YOUR DINO

GYROSPHERE

DINO DISCOVERY

Using the visual clues in the boxes below, circle the name of the dinosaur that you think you discovered. (ANSWER BELOW)

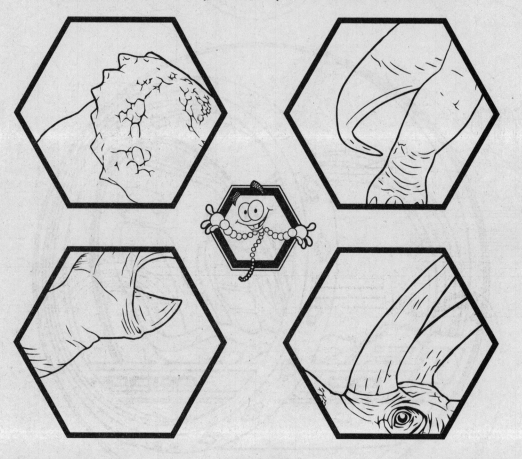

ANKYLOSAURUS

VELOCIRAPTOR

TRICERATOPS

TM & © Universal and Amblin

DNA SEQUENCE

HYBRID

RAPTOR: ECHO

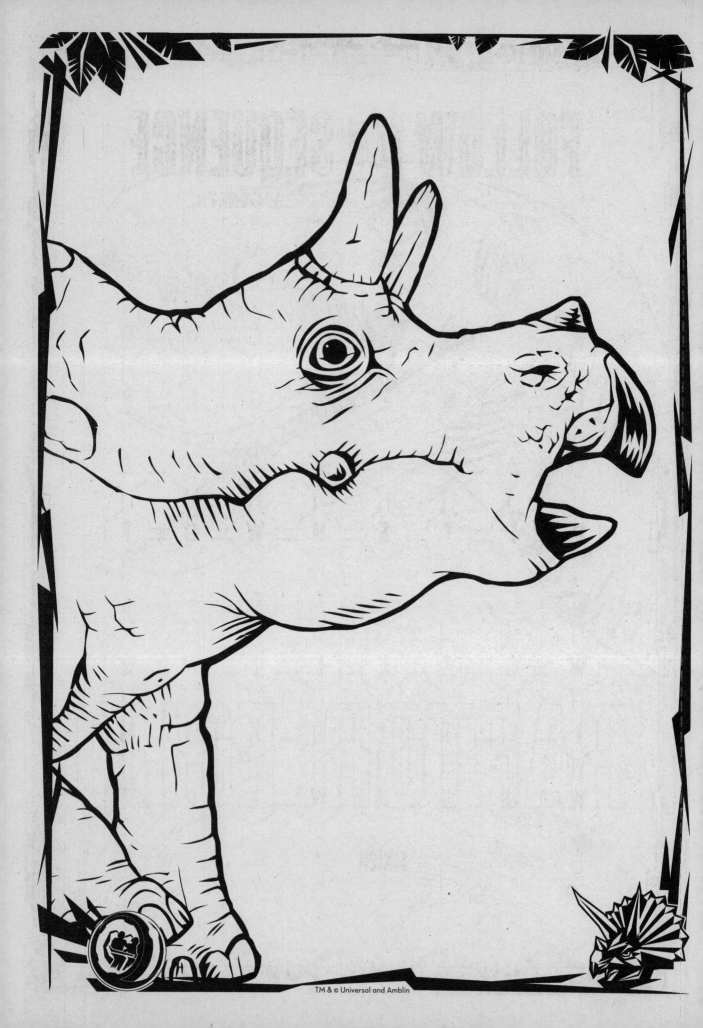

TM & © Universal and Amblin

FOLLOW THE SEQUENCE

Using the letters, in order, from the word **GENETIC**,
follow the correct path to find your way through the maze.

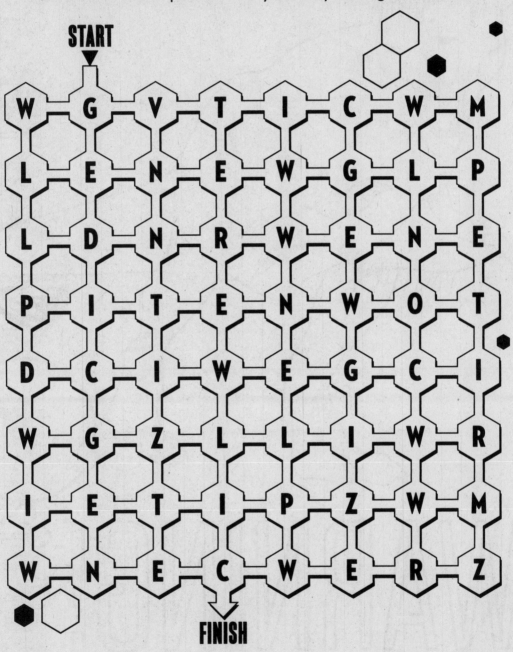

START

FINISH

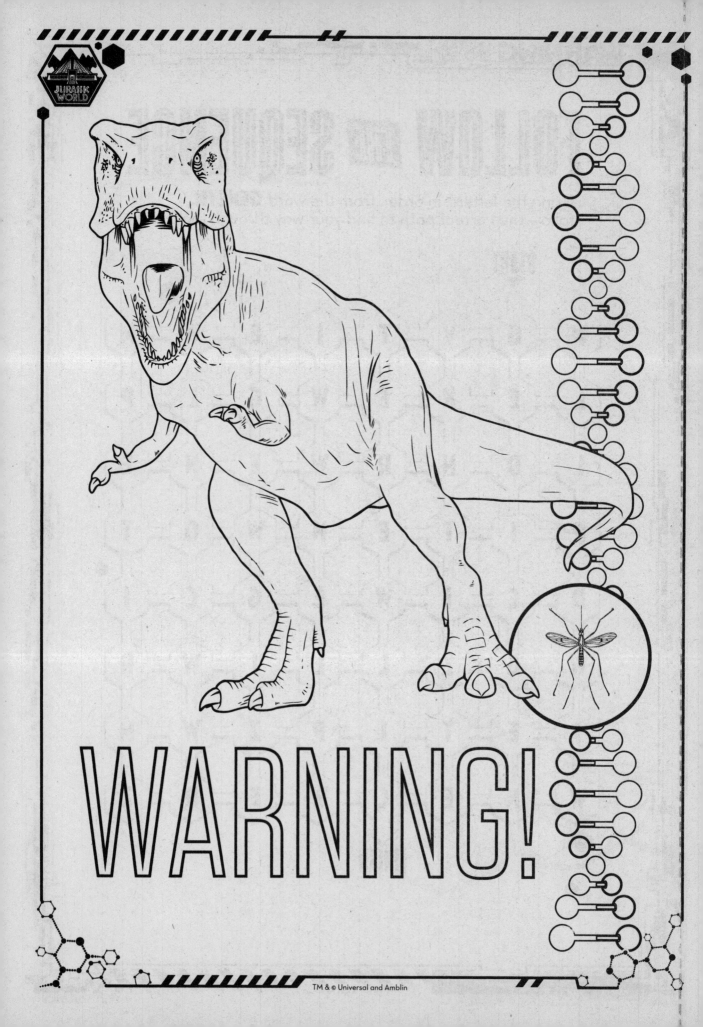

WARNING!

CREATION LAB

Draw a new dinosaur by splicing these two dinos together. Will yours have more armor, more teeth, or a longer tail? You decide!

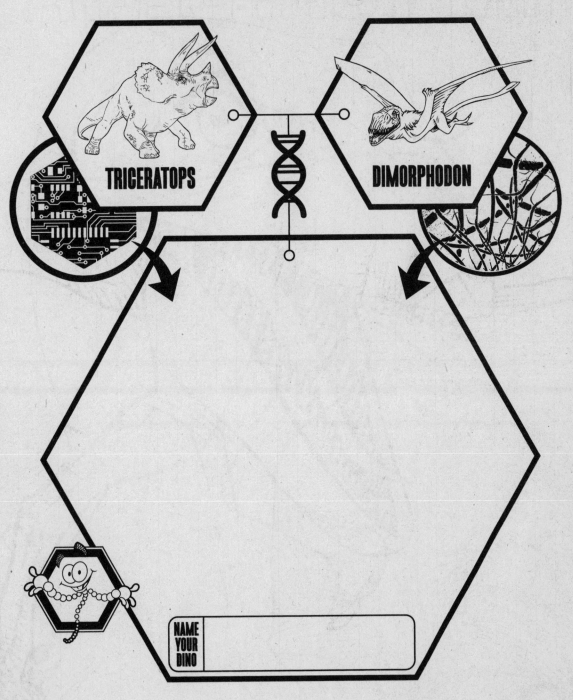

TRICERATOPS

DIMORPHODON

NAME YOUR DINO

RAPTOR: DELTA

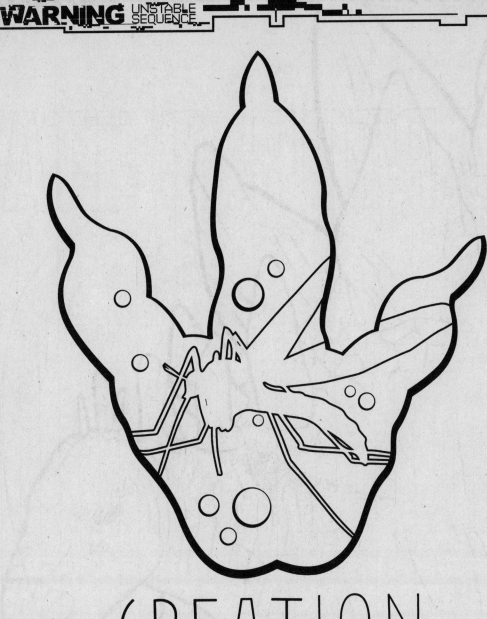

CREATION LAB

SEE LIFE RECREATED

JURASSIC WORLD™

DINO DISCOVERY

Using the visual clues in the boxes below, circle the name of the dinosaur that you think you discovered. (ANSWER BELOW)

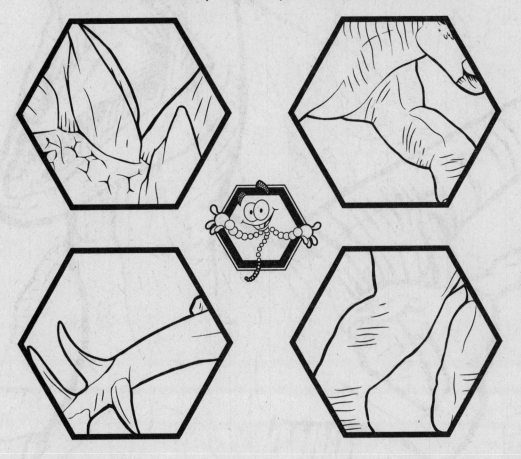

STEGOSAURUS

BABY TRICERATOPS

VELOCIRAPTOR

(ANSWER: STEGOSAURUS)

TM & © Universal and Amblin

FOLLOW THE SEQUENCE

Using the letters, in order, from the word **FUSION**,
follow the correct path to find your way through the maze.

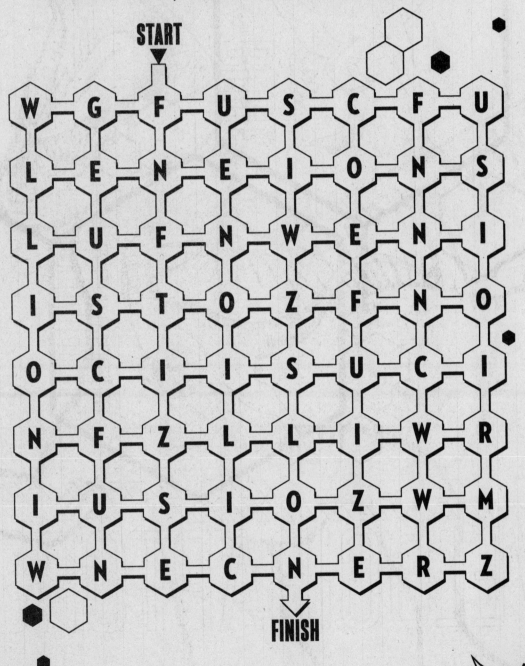

START

FINISH

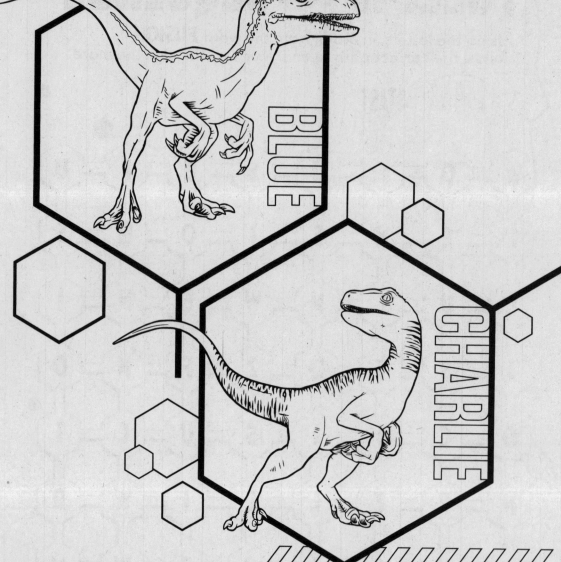

BLUE

CHARLIE

VELOCIRAPTORS

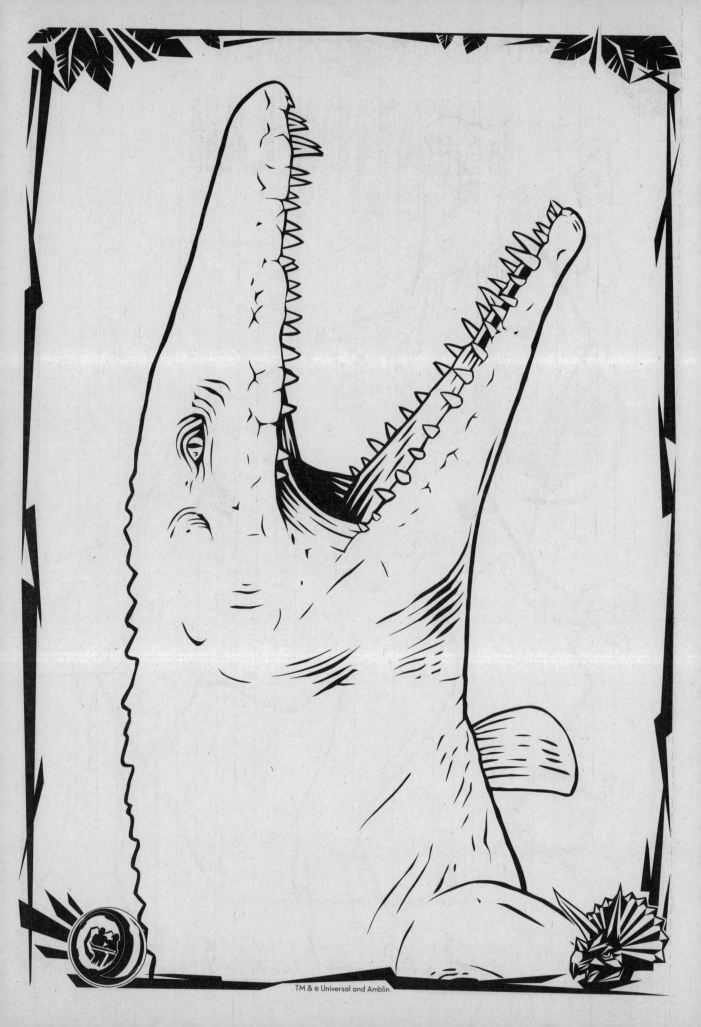

TM & © Universal and Amblin

CREATION LAB

Draw a new dinosaur by splicing these two dinos together. Will yours have more armor, more teeth, or a longer tail? You decide!

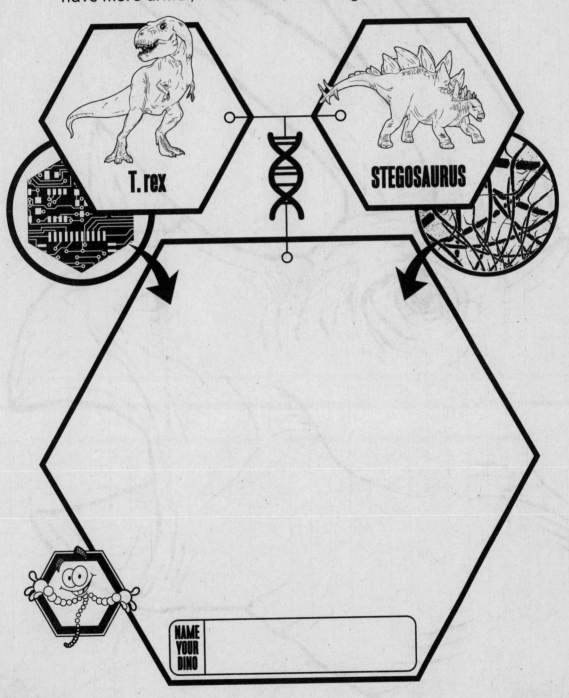

T. rex

STEGOSAURUS

NAME
YOUR
DINO

WARNING UNSTABLE SEQUENCE

TM & © Universal and Amblin

RAPTOR: CHARLIE

TM & © Universal and Amblin

DINO DISCOVERY

Using the visual clues in the boxes below, circle the name
of the dinosaur that you think you discovered. (ANSWER BELOW)

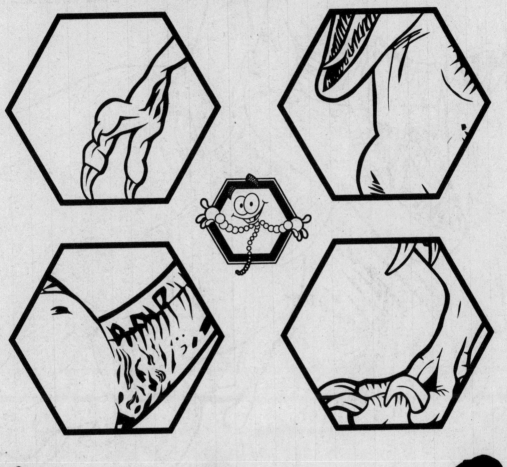

GALLIMIMUS

VELOCIRAPTOR

TYRANNOSAURUS REX

(ANSWER: VELOCIRAPTOR)

TM & © Universal and Amblin

STEGOSAURUS

FOLLOW THE SEQUENCE

Using the letters, in order, from the word **JURASSIC**,
follow the correct path to find your way through the maze.

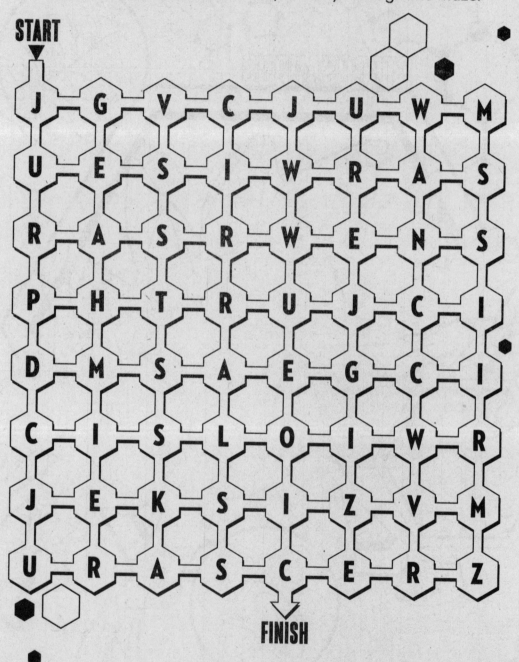

START

FINISH

ADVANCES
IN GENE SPLICING

RAPTOR: BLUE

CREATION LAB

Draw a new dinosaur by splicing these two dinos together. Will yours have more armor, more teeth, or a longer tail? You decide!

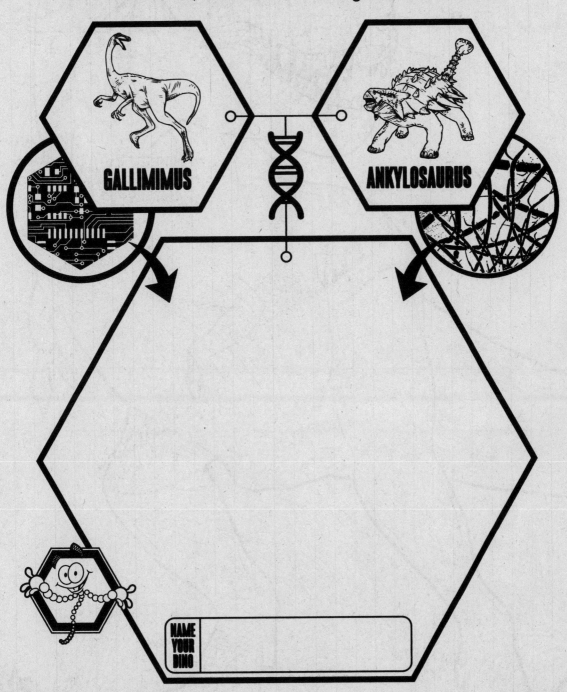

GALLIMIMUS

ANKYLOSAURUS

NAME YOUR DINO

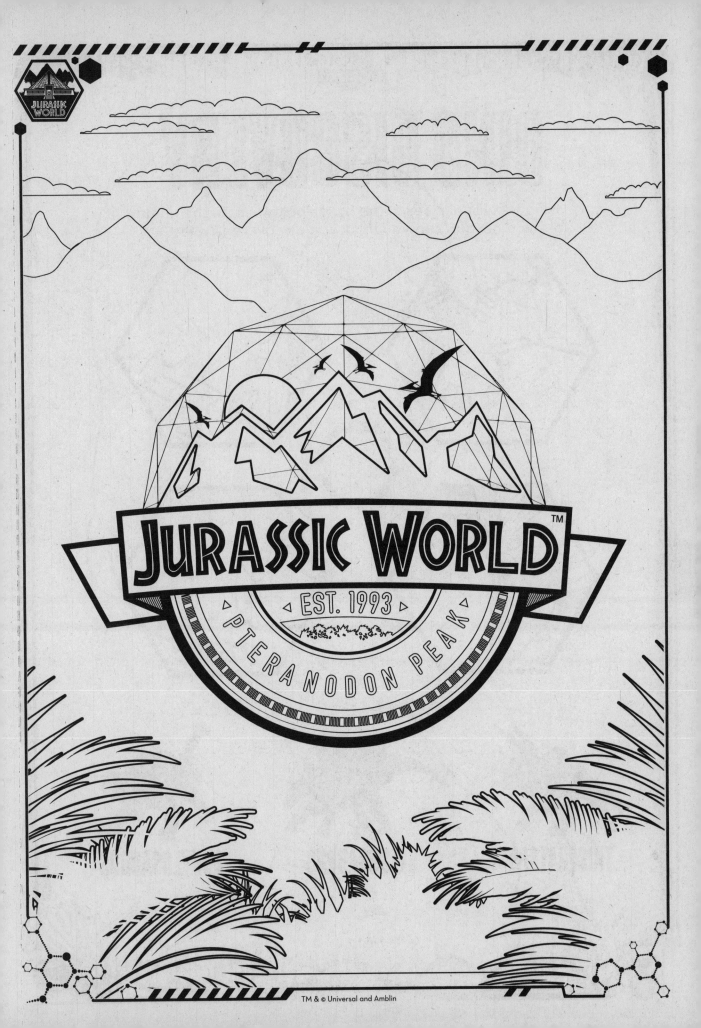

DINO DISCOVERY

Using the visual clues in the boxes below, circle the name of the dinosaur that you think you discovered. (ANSWER BELOW)

TRICERATOPS

STEGOSAURUS

ANKYLOSAURUS

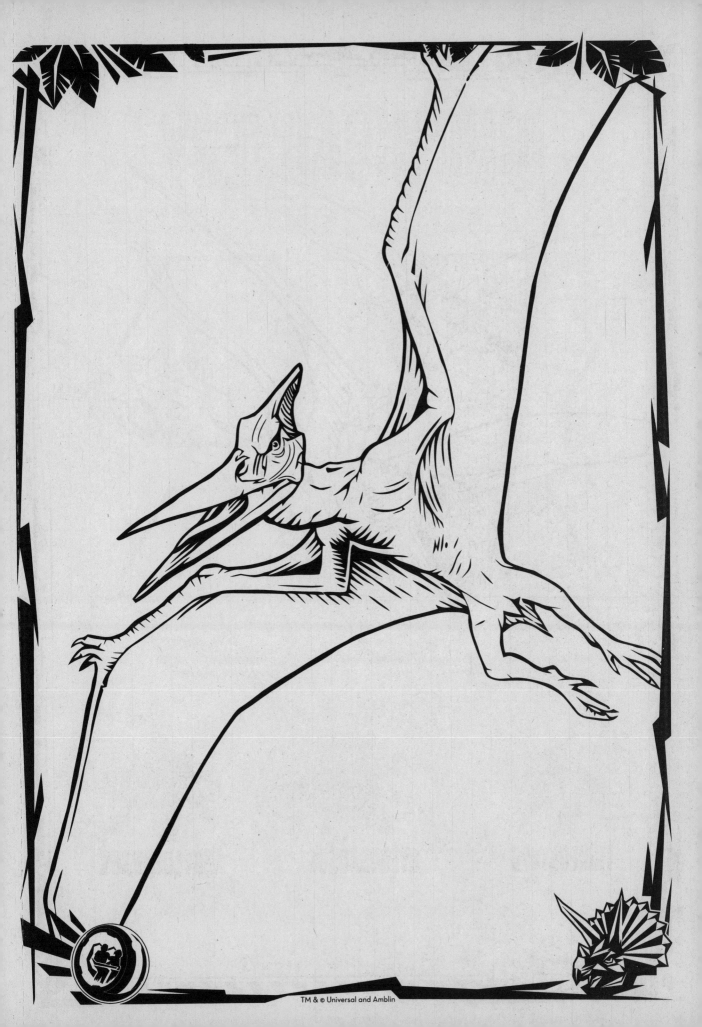

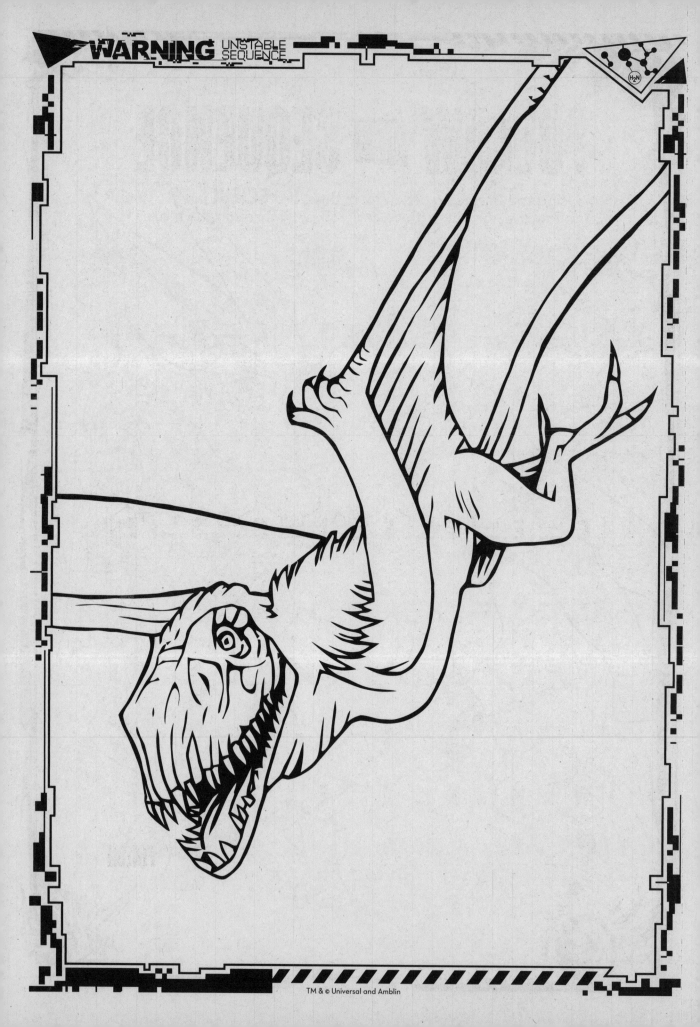

FOLLOW THE SEQUENCE

Using the letters, in order, from the word **SCIENCE**,
follow the correct path to find your way through the maze.

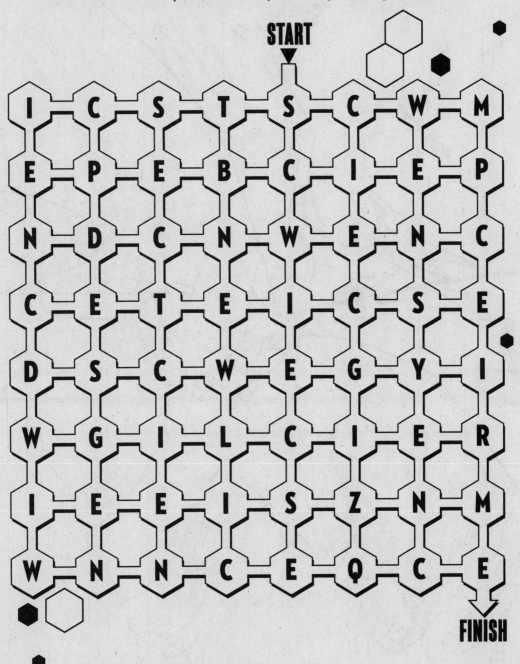

TM & © Universal and Amblin

TM & © Universal and Amblin

TM & © Universal and Amblin

FOLLOW THE SEQUENCE

Using the letters, in order, from the word **WARNING**, follow the correct path to find your way through the maze.

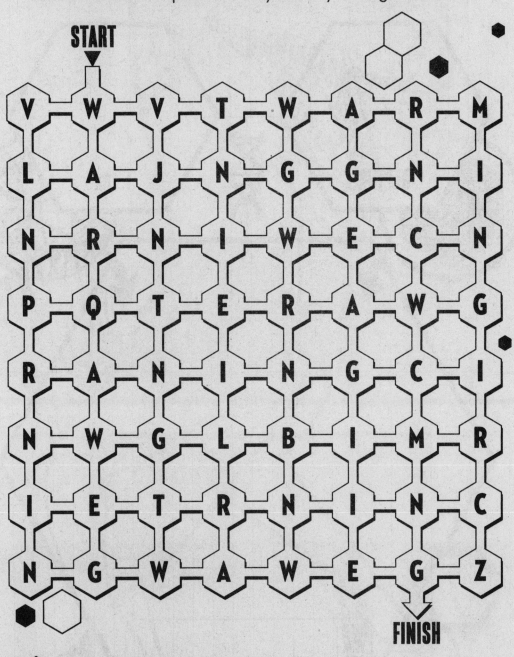

START

FINISH

CREATION LAB

Draw a new dinosaur by splicing these two dinos together. Will yours have more armor, more teeth, or a longer tail? You decide!

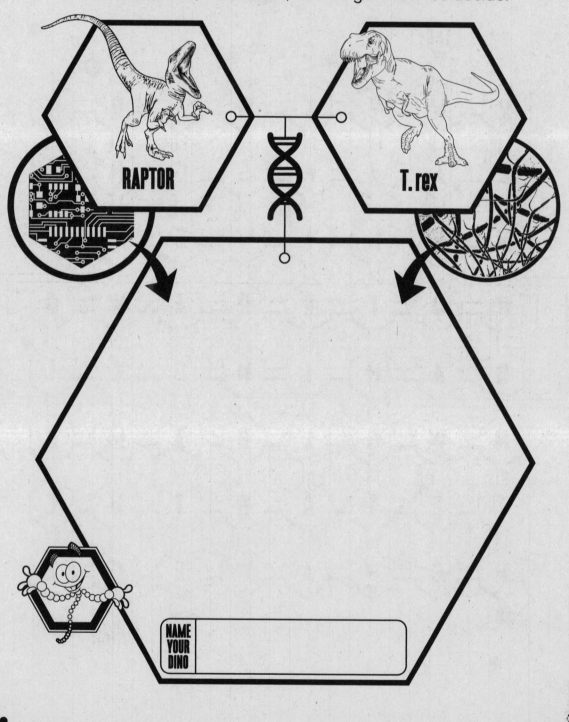

RAPTOR

T. rex

NAME YOUR DINO

DINO DISCOVERY

Using the visual clues in the boxes below, circle the name of the dinosaur that you think you discovered. (ANSWER BELOW)

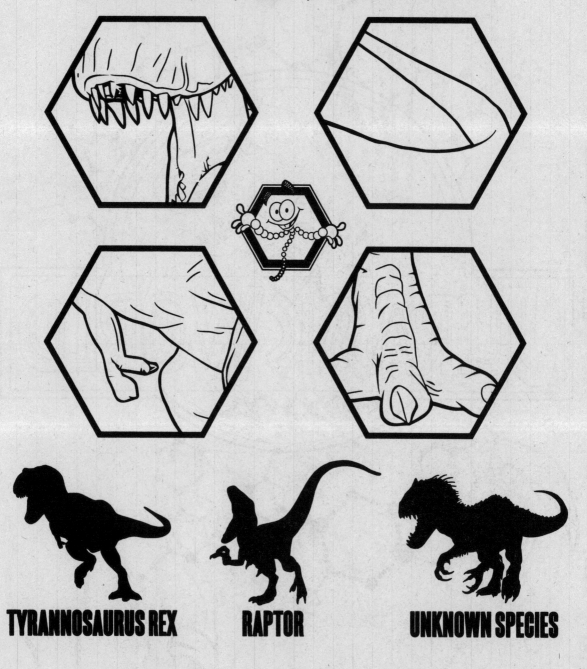

TYRANNOSAURUS REX **RAPTOR** **UNKNOWN SPECIES**

(ANSWER: TYRANNOSAURUS REX)

TM & © Universal and Amblin

TM & © Universal and Amblin